PIANO / VOCAL / GUITAR

budgetbooks

COUNTRY SONGS

Exclusive Distributors:
Music Sales Limited
8/9 Frith Street, London W1D 3JB, England.
Music Sales Pty Limited
120 Rothschild Avenue, Rosebery, NSW 2018, Australia.

Order No. HLE90001901
ISBN 1-84449-106-4
This book © Copyright 2003 by Hal Leonard Europe

Printed in the USA

Your Guarantee of Quality
As publishers, we strive to produce every book to the highest commercial standards.
The book has been carefully designed to minimise awkward page turns and to make playing from it a real pleasure.
Throughout, the printing and binding have been planned to ensure a sturdy, attractive publication which should give years of enjoyment.
If your copy fails to meet our high standards, please inform us and we will gladly replace it.

www.musicsales.com

Hal Leonard Europe
Distributed by Music Sales

CONTENTS

ABILENE

Words and Music by LESTER BROWN,
JOHN D. LOUDERMILK and BOB GIBSON

Ab - i - lene, __ Ab - i - lene, __ pret - ti - est town I've ev - er seen. __ Wom - en there __ don't treat you mean __ in Ab - i - lene, my Ab - i - lene.

ANY OLD TIME

Words and Music by
JIMMIE RODGERS

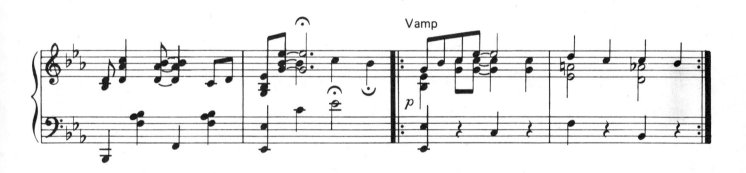

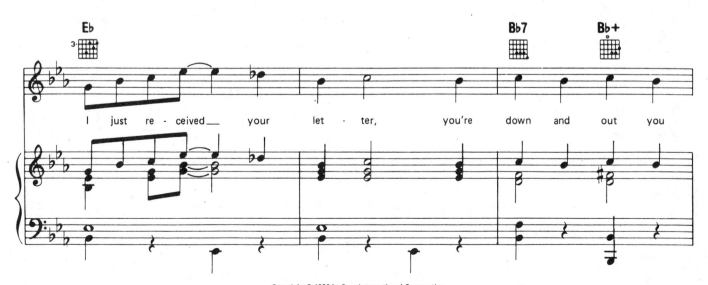

I just re-ceived___ your let-ter, you're down and out you

say, at first I thought I would tell you to tra-vel on the oth-er way, but in my mem-o-ry lin-gers, all you once were___ to me I'm going to give you an-oth-er chance___ to prove what you can

ACT NATURALLY

Words and Music by VONIE MORRISON
and JOHNNY RUSSELL

ALIBIS

Words and Music by
RANDY BOUDREAUX

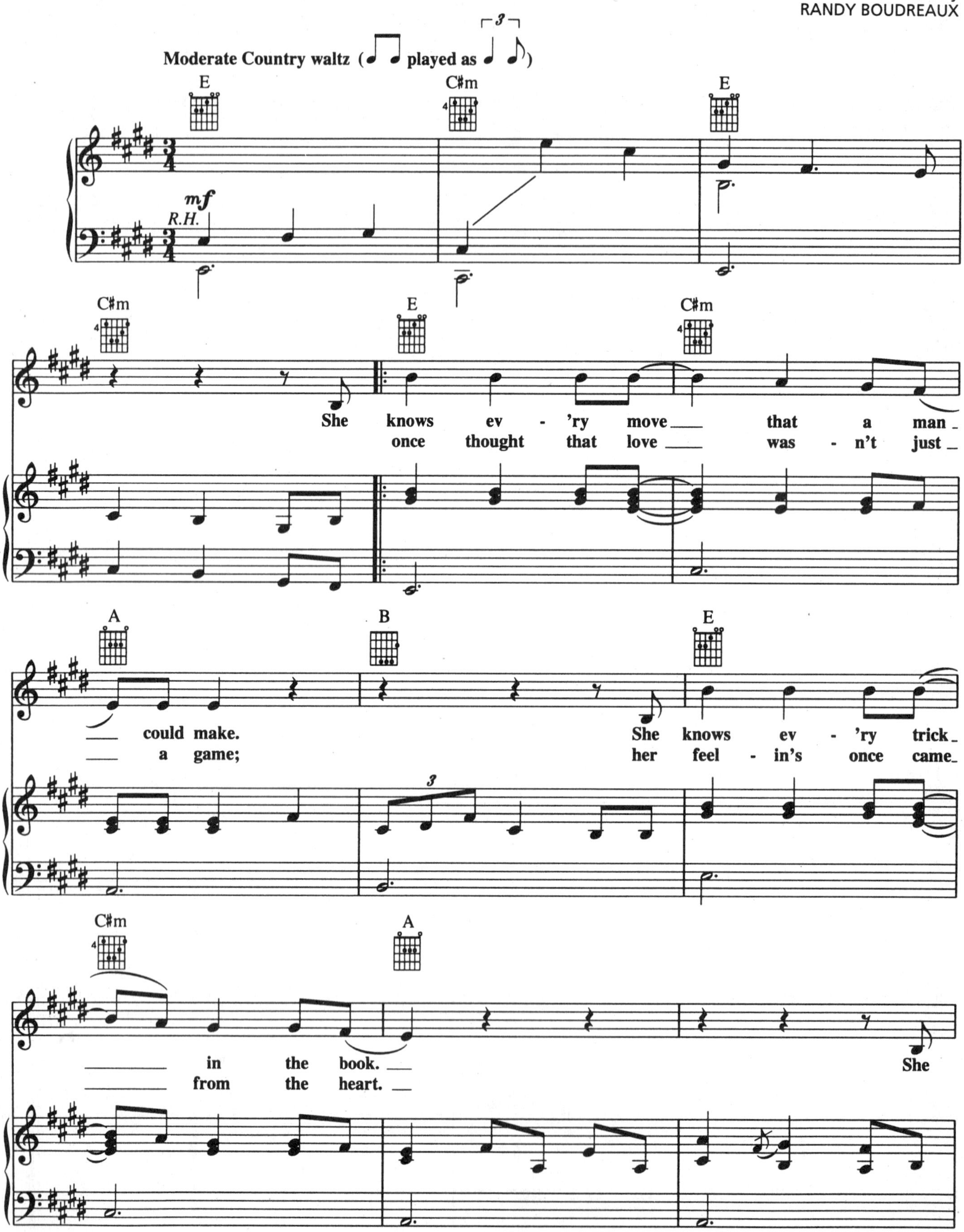

Moderate Country waltz (played as)
E
C#m
E
mf
R.H.
C#m
E
C#m
She knows ev - 'ry move ___ that a man ___
once thought that love ___ was - n't just ___
A
B
E
___ could make.
___ a game;
She knows ev - 'ry trick ___
her feel - in's once came ___
C#m
A
___ in the book. ___
___ from the heart. ___
She

ALL MY EX'S LIVE IN TEXAS

Words and Music by LYNDIA J. SHAFER
and SANGER D. SHAFER

ASKING US TO DANCE

Words and Music by
HUGH PRESTWOOD

There's a full moon up and ris-ing.

And there's a whis-per of a breeze

blow-ing through the tan-gled

AUCTIONEER

Words and Music by LEROY VAN DYKE
and BUDDY BLACK

(Spoken:) Hey, well all right, Sir, here we go there, and what're ya gonna give for 'em. I'm bid twenty-five, will ya gimme thirty, make it thirty, bid it to buy 'em at thirty dollars on 'er, will ya gimme thirty, now five, who woulda bid it at five, make it five, five bid and now forty dollars on 'er to buy 'em there...

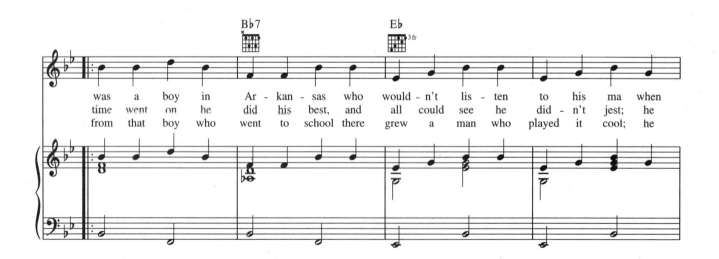

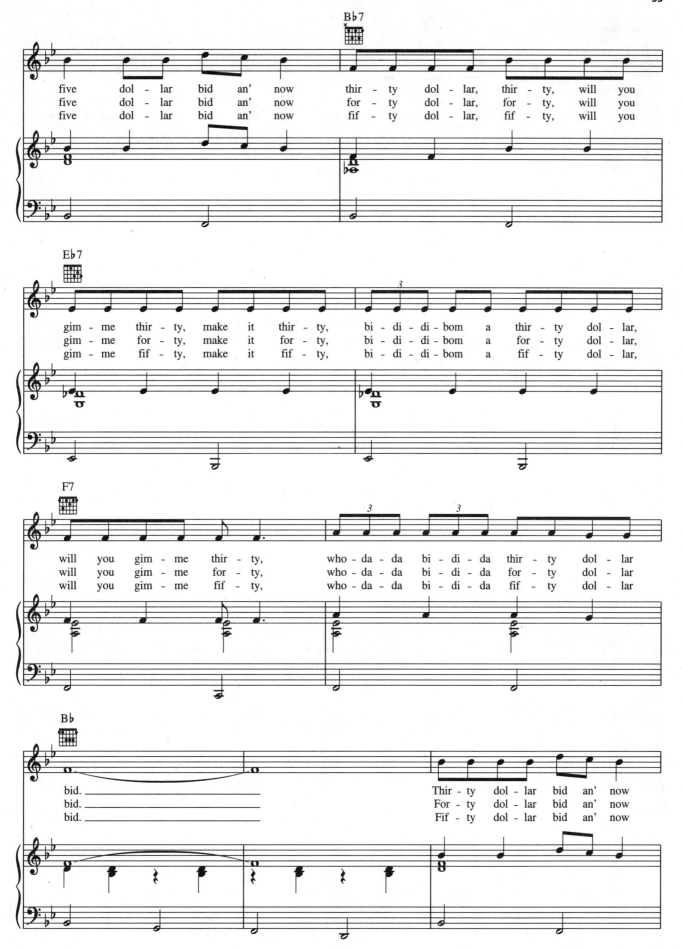

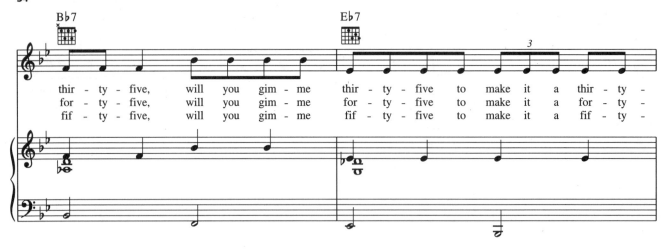

thir – ty – five, will you gim – me thir – ty – five to make it a thir – ty –
for – ty – five, will you gim – me for – ty – five to make it a for – ty –
fif – ty – five, will you gim – me fif – ty – five to make it a fif – ty –

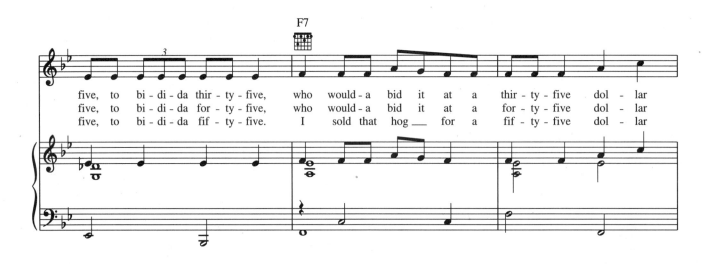

five, to bi – di – da thir – ty – five, who would – a bid it at a thir – ty – five dol – lar
five, to bi – di – da for – ty – five, who would – a bid it at a for – ty – five dol – lar
five, to bi – di – da fif – ty – five. I sold that hog ___ for a fif – ty – five dol – lar

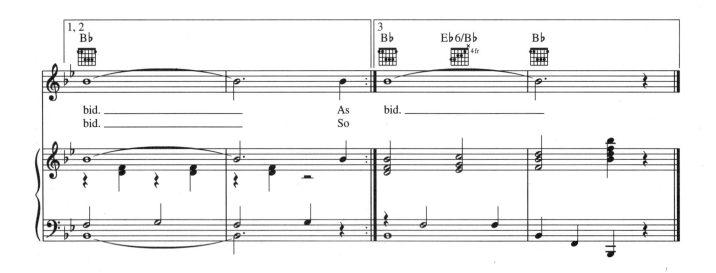

bid. _____ As bid. _____
bid. _____ So

(Spoken:) *Hey, well all right, Sir, open the gate an' let 'em out and walk 'em, boys! Here we come with lot number 29 in, what'd ya gonna give for 'em? I'm bid twenty-five, will ya gimme thirty, make it thirty, bid it to buy 'em at thirty dollars on 'er, will you gimme thirty dollars on 'er, now five, thirty-five, an' now the forty dollars on 'er, will you gimme forty, make it forty, now five, forty-five an' now the fifty dollars on 'er, will you gimme fifty, now five, fifty-five, an' now the sixty dollars on 'er, will you gimme sixty, make it sixty, now five, who'd-a bid it at sixty dollars on 'er to buy 'em there...*

BLUE EYES CRYING IN THE RAIN

Words and Music by
FRED ROSE

BIG BAD JOHN

Words and Music by
JIMMY DEAN

Verse 1. Every morning at the mine you could see him arrive,
He stood six-foot-six and weighed two-forty-five.
Kind of broad at the shoulder and narrow at the hip,
And everybody knew you didn't give no lip to Big John!
(Refrain)

Verse 2. Nobody seemed to know where John called home,
He just drifted into town and stayed all alone.
He didn't say much, a-kinda quiet and shy,
And if you spoke at all, you just said, "Hi" to Big John!
Somebody said he came from New Orleans,
Where he got in a fight over a Cajun queen.
And a crashing blow from a huge right hand
Sent a Louisiana fellow to the promised land. Big John!
(Refrain)

Verse 3. Then came the day at the bottom of the mine
When a timber cracked and the men started crying.
Miners were praying and hearts beat fast,
And everybody thought that they'd breathed their last 'cept John.
Through the dust and the smoke of this man-made hell
Walked a giant of a man that the miners knew well.
Grabbed a sagging timber and gave out with a groan,
And, like a giant oak tree, just stood there alone. Big John!
(Refrain)

Verse 4. And with all of his strength, he gave a mighty shove;
Then a miner yelled out, "There's a light up above!"
And twenty men scrambled from a would-be grave,
And now there's only one left down there to save; Big John!
With jacks and timbers they started back down
Then came that rumble way down in the ground,
And smoke and gas belched out of that mine,
Everybody knew it was the end of the line for Big John!
(Refrain)

Verse 5. Now they never re-opened that worthless pit,
They just placed a marble stand in front of it;
These few words are written on that stand:
"At the bottom of this mine lies a big, big man; Big John!"
(Refrain)

Blue

Words and Music by
BILL MACK

BLUE MOON OF KENTUCKY

Words and Music by
BILL MONROE

Bright jump tempo

Blue

moon, _____ blue moon, _____ blue

moon _____ keep a-shin-in' bright. _____ Blue

BONAPARTE'S RETREAT

Words and Music by REDD STEWART
and PEE WEE KING

BORN TO LOSE

Words and Music by
TED DAFFAN

BOOT SCOOTIN' BOOGIE

Words and Music by
RONNIE DUNN

BREATHE

Words and Music by HOLLY LAMAR
and STEPHANIE BENTLEY

Moderately fast

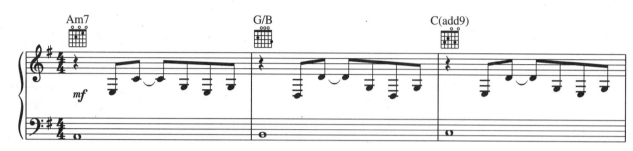

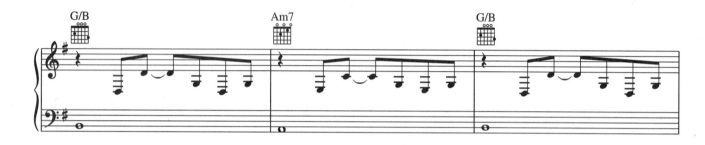

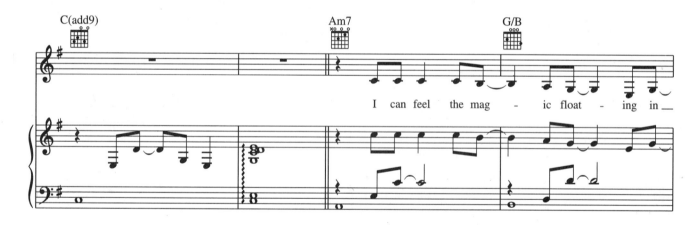

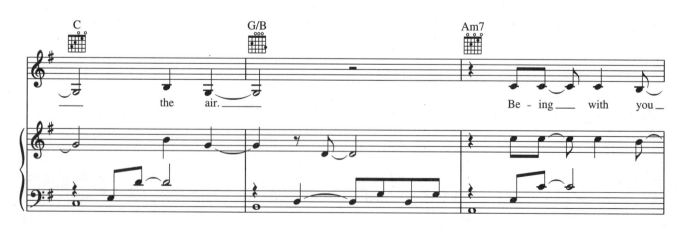

THE CHAIR

Words and Music by HANK COCHRAN
and DEAN DILLON

Medium Slow

Well, ex- cuse ___ me, ___ but I think you've ___ got my

chair. No, that ___ one's not tak - en; I ___ don't

mind if you ___ sit here. I'll be glad to share. Yeah, it's u-

COLD, COLD HEART

Words and Music by
HANK WILLIAMS

COWBOY TAKE ME AWAY

Words and Music by MARTIE SEIDEL
and MARCUS HUMMON

Original key: F# major. This edition has been transposed up one half-step to be more playable.

CRAZY

Words and Music by
WILLIE NELSON

D-I-V-O-R-C-E

Words and Music by BOBBY BRADDOCK
and CURLY PUTMAN

CRYIN' TIME

Words and Music by
BUCK OWENS

Now they say that ab-sence makes the heart grow fon-der,___ And that tears are on-ly rain to make love grow

Well, my love for you could nev-er grow no strong-er,___ If I lived to be a hund-red years

old. Oh, it's cry-in' time a-gain, you're gon-na leave me,___ I can see that far a-way look ___ in your

DEEP IN THE HEART OF TEXAS

Words by JUNE HERSHEY
Music by DON SWANDER

B♭/D
C7
land I un - der - stand, and it's
F
F7/E♭
B♭/D
G9
C7
E♭7
C7
there I long to be. The
F6
stars at night are big and
coy - otes wail a - long the
bright, deep in the heart of
trail, deep in the heart of
(Clap Clap Clap Clap)

Tex - as; _____ The prai - rie
Tex - as; _____ The rab - bits

sky   is   wide   and   high,
rush   a - round the   brush,
                                            (Clap   Clap   Clap

deep   in   the   heart   of   Tex - as. _____
deep   in   the   heart   of   Tex - as. _____
Clap)

___ The   sage   in   bloom   is   like   per -
___ The   cow - boys   cry,   "Ki - yip - pee -

C7

fume,
yi,"
(Clap Clap Clap Clap)
deep in the heart
deep in the heart
of Tex - as;
of Tex - as;

Re - minds me of the
The dog - ies bawl, and

one I love,
bawl I and bawl,
(Clap Clap Clap Clap)
deep in the heart of
deep in the heart of

1 F   Gm7   C7
Tex - as.

2 F   Bb6   F
The Tex - as.

8vb

ELVIRA

Words and Music by
DALLAS FRAZIER

Verse 2. Tonight I'm gonna meet her
At the hungry house cafe
And I'm gonna give her all the love I can
She's gonna jump and holler
'Cause I saved up my last two dollar
And we're gonna search and find that preacher man
Chorus

FOR THE GOOD TIMES

Words and Music by
KRIS KRISTOFFERSON

FRIENDS IN LOW PLACES

Words and Music by DEWAYNE BLACKWELL
and EARL BUD LEE

FUNNY HOW TIME SLIPS AWAY

Words and Music by
WILLIE NELSON

THE GAMBLER

Words and Music by
DON SCHLITZ

GENTLE ON MY MIND

Words and Music by
JOHN HARTFORD

1. It's know-ing that your door is al - ways o - pen and your
2.- 4.(See additional lyrics)

path is free to walk   that

makes me tend to leave my sleep - ing bag rolled up and stashed be - hind your

rivers of my mem-'ry that keeps you ev-er gentle on my mind.

It's

mind.

Additional Lyrics

2. It's not clinging to the rocks and ivy planted on their columns now that binds me,
   Or something that somebody said because they thought we fit together walkin'.
   It's just knowing that the world will not be cursing or forgiving when I walk along
   Some railroad track and find
   That you're moving on the backroads by the rivers of my memory, and for hours
   You're just gentle on my mind.

3. Though the wheat fields and the clotheslines and junkyards and the highways
   Come between us,
   And some other woman crying to her mother 'cause she turned and I was gone.
   I still run in silence, tears of joy might stain my face and summer sun might
   Burn me 'til I'm blind,
   But not to where I cannot see you walkin' on the backroads by the rivers flowing
   Gentle on my mind.

4. I dip my cup of soup back from the gurglin' cracklin' caldron in some train yard,
   My beard a roughening coal pile and a dirty hat pulled low across my face.
   Through cupped hands 'round a tin can I pretend I hold you to my breast and find
   That you're waving from the backroads by the rivers of my memory, ever smilin',
   Ever gentle on my mind.

GAMES PEOPLE PLAY

Words and Music by
JOE SOUTH

GONE COUNTRY

Words and Music by
BOB McDILL

She's been play-ing that ___ room ___ on the strip
folk scene's ___ dead, ___ but
mutes to L. A., ___ but

for ten years in Ve-gas.
he's hold-ing out ___ in the vil-lage.
he's got a house ___ in the Val-ley.

Ev-'ry night she looks ___ in the mir-ror, and she on-ly
He's been writ-ing songs, ___ speak-ing out a-gainst wealth and
But the bills are pil-ing up, ___ and the pop scene just ain't gon-na

HAPPY TRAILS

from the Television Series THE ROY ROGERS SHOW

Words and Music by
DALE EVANS

GRANDPA
(Tell Me 'Bout the Good Old Days)

Words and Music by
JAMIE O'HARA

HARD ROCK BOTTOM OF YOUR HEART

Words and Music by
HUGH PRESTWOOD

HELLO WALLS

Words and Music by
WILLIE NELSON

HE STOPPED LOVING HER TODAY

Words and Music by BOBBY BRADDOCK
and CURLY PUTMAN

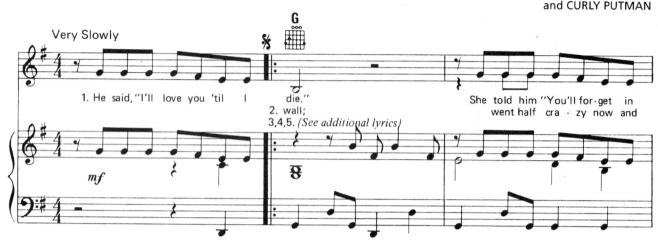

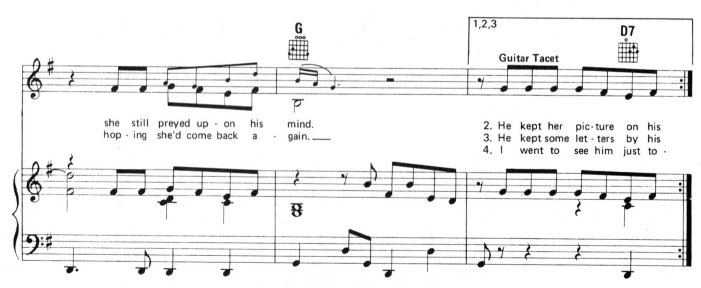

Verse 3:
He kept some letters by his bed, dated 1962.
He had underlined in red every single, "I love you".

Verse 4:
I went to see him just today, oh, but I didn't see no tears;
All dressed up to go away, first time I'd seen him smile in years.
(To Chorus:)

Verse 5: *(Spoken)*
You know, she came to see him one last time.
We all wondered if she would.
And it came running through my mind,
This time he's over her for good. (To Chorus:)

HERE'S A QUARTER
(Call Someone Who Cares)

Words and Music by
TRAVIS TRITT

lone - some _____ and scared. _____
me _____ un - a - ware. _____

And you say you'd be _____
But the fact is _____ you've _____

hap - py if you could just _____ come back
run. _____ Girl, _____ that can't _____ be un - done.

home. _____ Well, here's a quar - ter. _____ Call _____
So here's a quar - ter. _____ Call _____

HEY, GOOD LOOKIN'

Words and Music by
HANK WILLIAMS

Moderately

I CAN LOVE YOU LIKE THAT

Words and Music by MARIBETH DERRY,
JENNIFER KIMBALL and STEVE DIAMOND

I CAN'T STOP LOVING YOU

Words and Music by
DON GIBSON

(I Never Promised You A)
ROSE GARDEN

Words and Music by
JOE SOUTH

I beg your par-don, I nev-er prom-ised you a rose ___ gar-den.

A-long with the sun-shine, there's got to be a lit-tle rain_ some-time.

When you take you got to give, so live and let live ___ or let

go, oh, oh, oh. ___ I beg your par - don,

I nev - er prom-ised you a rose ___ gar - den.

1. I could
2.
3. I could
4.

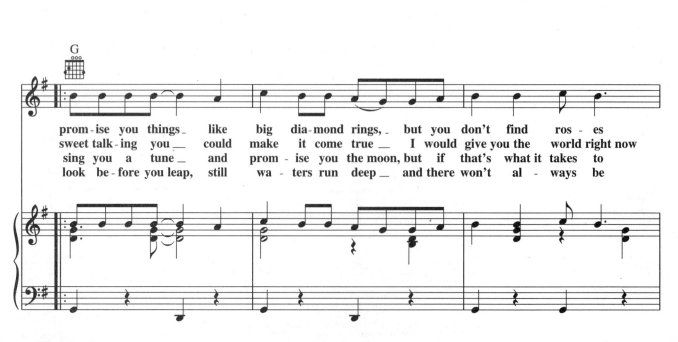

prom - ise you things ___ like big dia-mond rings, ___ but you don't find ros - es
sweet talk-ing you ___ could make it come true ___ I would give you the world right now
sing you a tune ___ and prom - ise you the moon, but if that's what it takes to
look be-fore you leap, still wa - ters run deep ___ and there won't al - ways be

I FALL TO PIECES

Words and Music by HANK COCHRAN
and HARLAN HOWARD

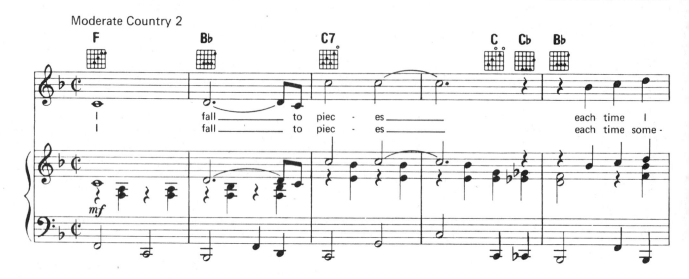

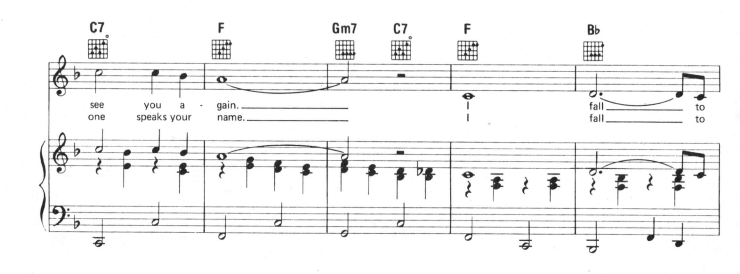

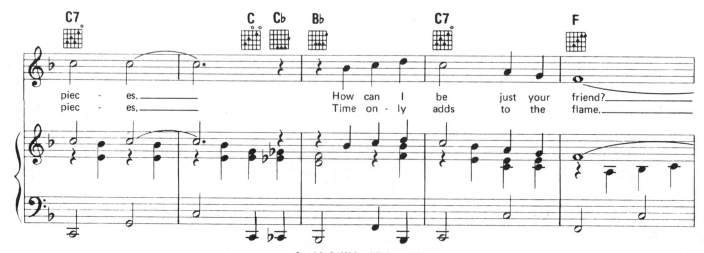

I OVERLOOKED AN ORCHID

Words and Music by CARL STORY,
CARL SMITH and SHIRLY LYN

I'LL FORGIVE YOU
(But I Can't Forget)

Words and Music by J.L. FRANK
and PEE WEE KING

Moderato waltz tempo

Some-where I hope you are hap-py;
sad- ness of our part - ing still lin - gers;
that you have left me for an - oth - er;

I hope your heart holds no re - gret;
My eyes from that tears are still wet;
What a pi - ty that we ev - er met;

Each night I pray the Lord to watch for
I'll al - ways love you
For life ain't worth liv - ing with -

I WALK THE LINE

Words and Music by
JOHN R. CASH

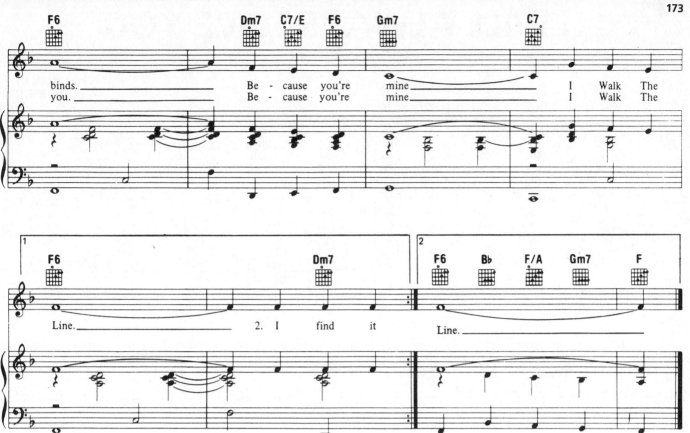

3. As sure as night is dark and day is light,
   I keep you on my mind both day and night.
   And happiness I've known proves that it's right.
   Because you're mine I Walk The Line.

4. You've got a way to keep me on your side.
   You give me cause for love that I can't hide.
   For you I know I'd even try to turn the tide.
   Because you're mine I Walk The Line.

5. I keep a close watch on this heart of mine.
   I keep my eyes wide open all the time.
   I keep the ends out for the tie that binds.
   Because you're mine I Walk The Line.

I WILL ALWAYS LOVE YOU

Words and Music by
DOLLY PARTON

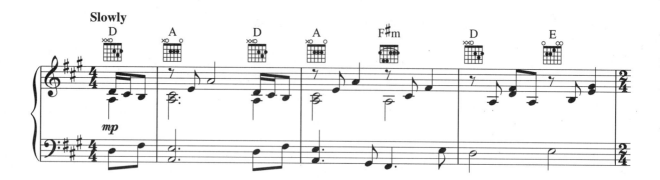

If I should _ stay, I would on - ly be in ___ your

sweet mem - o - ries, that's all I ___ am tak - ing with

hope *life treats you kind* *and I hope that you have all that you*

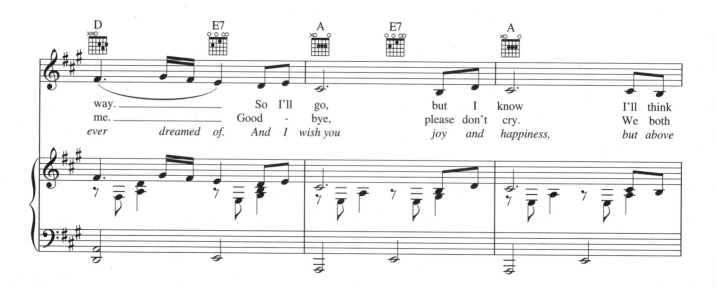

way. So I'll go, but I know I'll think

me. ___ Good - bye, please don't cry. We both

ever dreamed of. And I wish you *joy and happiness,* *but above*

I'M ALREADY THERE

Words and Music by RICHIE McDONALD,
FRANK MYERS and GARY BAKER

called her on the road from a lone-ly, cold ho-tel room just to

hear her say "I love you" one more time. And

I'M SO LONESOME I COULD CRY

Words and Music by
HANK WILLIAMS

I'VE COME TO EXPECT IT FROM YOU

Words and Music by DEAN DILLON
and BUDDY CANNON

Moderate Two-Beat

1. So up - set,
2. A mil - lion times,
3. *Instrumental*
4. I could raise hell,

A nerv - ous wreck. can't be - lieve___ you said___ good - bye.
A mil - lion lines _____ and I bought 'em ev - 'ry - one.
But what the hell, ___ it would - n't do a bit ___ of good. ___

MCA music publishing

Sit and smoke,
You don't care.
Pack and leave,

cry and joke
You rip and
my heart a-

a - bout ___ these tears in ___ my eyes. ___
tear ___ ev-'ry dream I've count - ed on. ___
grees it seems to think that ___ I should. ___

1., 3. How could you do what you've
2. I guess that I_____ should thank_____ my
4. There won't be_____ no more

gone and done to me?_____ I would-n't
un - luck - y stars_____ that I'm a - live
next time do - in' me wrong._____ You'll come

treat a dog ___ the way ___ you treat - ed me.
back this time ___ and to find ___ you're the way ___ out you are.
that I'm gone.

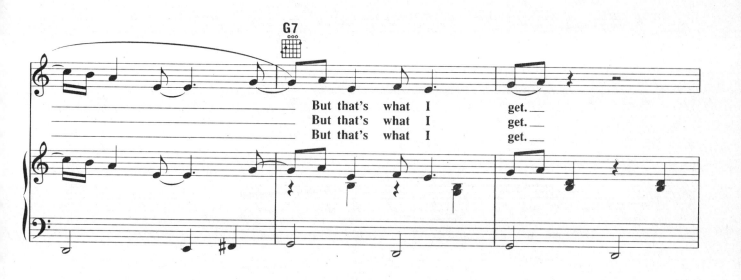

But that's what I get. ___
But that's what I get. ___
But that's what I get. ___

I've come to ex - pect ___ it ___ from you.
I've come to ex - pect ___ it ___ from you.
you should ex - pect ___ that ___ from me.

IF I SAID YOU HAVE A BEAUTIFUL BODY WOULD YOU HOLD IT AGAINST ME

Words and Music by
DAVID BELLAMY

dy-ing of thirst,—would your flow-ing love—come quench— me?—   If I said—

—you have a beau-ti-ful bod - y, would you hold it a-gainst— me?—

VERSE

Now, we could talk all night———— a - bout the weath - er;———
Now, rain can fall so soft———— a - gainst the win - dow;———

could tell you 'bout my friends——— out on the
the sun can shine so bright——— up in the

IT WASN'T GOD WHO MADE HONKY TONK ANGELS

Words and Music by
J.D. MILLER

listen to the words you are say - ing, ____
start most ev - 'ry heart that's ev - er bro - ken ____

____ it brings mem - 'ries when I was a trust - ing
____ was be - cause there al - ways was a man to

wife. ____ } It was - n't God who made
blame. ____

hon - ky tonk an - gels, ____ as you

JEALOUS HEART

Words and Music by
JENNY LOU CARSON

THE KEEPER OF THE STARS

Words and Music by KAREN STALEY,
DANNY MAYO and DICKEY LEE

LAST DATE

By FLOYD CRAMER

A LITTLE BITTY TEAR

Words and Music by
HANK COCHRAN

1. When you said you were leav-ing to-mor-row, That to-
2. said I'd laugh when you left me, Pull a
3. thing went like I planned it, And I

day was our last day; I said there'd be no
fun-ny as you went out the door; That I'd have an-oth-er one
real-ly put on quite a show. In my heart I felt I could

sor-row, That I'd laugh when you walked a-way.
wait-ing I'd wave good-bye as you go.
stand it, Till you walked with your grip thru the door.

LONGNECK BOTTLE

Words and Music by RICK CARNES
and STEVE WARINER

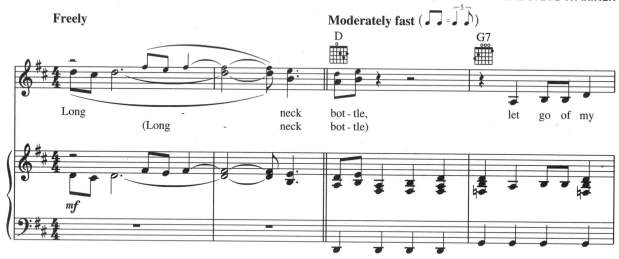

214

MI VIDA LOCA
(My Crazy Life)

Words and Music by PAM TILLIS
and JESS LEARY

Sweet -

LUCILLE

Words and Music by ROGER BOWLING
and HAL BYNUM

224

MAKE THE WORLD GO AWAY

Words and Music by
HANK COCHRAN

MAMMAS DON'T LET YOUR BABIES GROW UP TO BE COWBOYS

Words and Music by ED BRUCE
and PATSY BRUCE

Country Waltz

MY BEST FRIEND

Words and Music by AIMEE MAYO
and BILL LUTHER

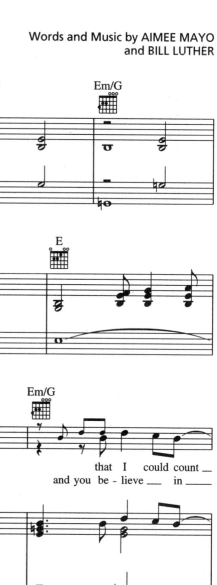

I nev-er had no one that I could count on.
You stand by me and you be-lieve in me

on. I've been let down so man-y times.
me like no-bod-y ev-er has.

NO DOUBT ABOUT IT

Words and Music by JOHN SCOTT SHERRILL
and STEVE SESKIN

NOBODY LOVES ME LIKE YOU DO

Words by PAMELA PHILLIPS
Music by JAMES P. DUNNE

Slowly, with expression

Female: Like a can - dle burn - ing bright,

love is glow - ing in __ your eyes. __

OH, LONESOME ME

Words and Music by
DON GIBSON

Ev - 'ry - bod - y's go - in' out and hav - in' fun_____ I'm
bad mis - take I'm mak - in' by just hang - in' round_____ I

just a fool for stay - in' home and hav - in' none_____ I
know that I should have some fun and paint the town_____ A

can't get o - ver how she set me free_____
love - sick fool that's blind and just can't see_____

OKIE FROM MUSKOGEE

Words and Music by MERLE HAGGARD
and ROY EDWARD BURRIS

1. We don't smoke mar-i-jua-na in Mus-ko-gee,_____
2. We don't make a par-ty out of lov-ing,_____
boots are still in style if a man needs foot-wear,_____

And we don't take our trips on L. S.
But we like hold-ing hands and pitch-ing
Beads and Ro-man san-dals won't be

Bb7

D.
woo.
seen.

And we don't burn our draft cards down on
We don't let our hair grow long and
Foot - ball's still the rough - est thing on

Main Street,
shag - gy
cam - pus,

But we like liv-ing right and be-ing
Like the hip-pies out in San Fran-cis-co
And the kids here still re-spect the Col-lege

Eb

free.
do.
Dean.

And I'm proud to be an

O - kie from Mus - ko - gee;

A

ONE MORE LAST CHANCE

Words and Music by GARY NICHOLSON
and VINCE GILL

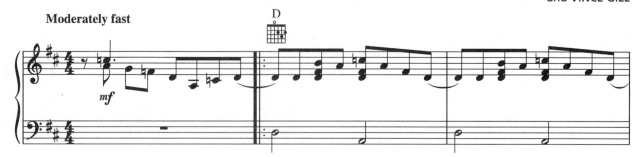

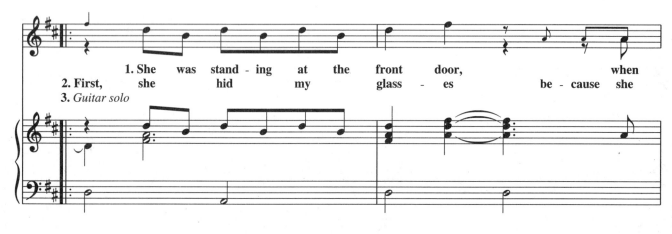

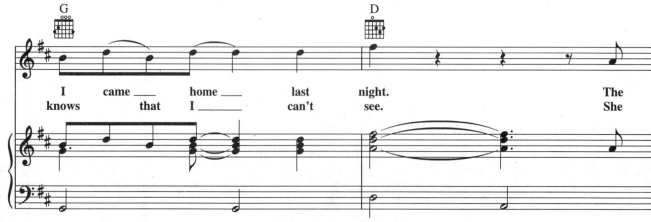

Give me just one more last chance ___ be -

fore you say ___ we're through. ___

Repeat ad lib. and Fade

PRETTY PAPER

Words and Music by
WILLIE NELSON

PLEASE REMEMBER ME

Words and Music by RODNEY CROWELL
and WILL JENNINGS

Original key: Db major. This edition has been transposed down one half-step to be more playable.

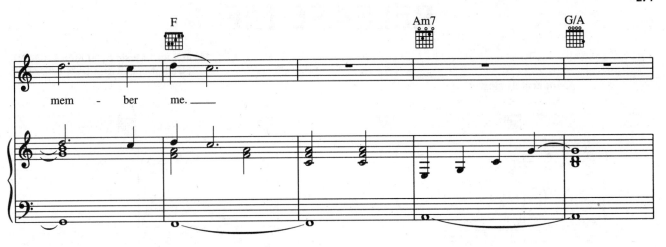

mem - ber me. ___

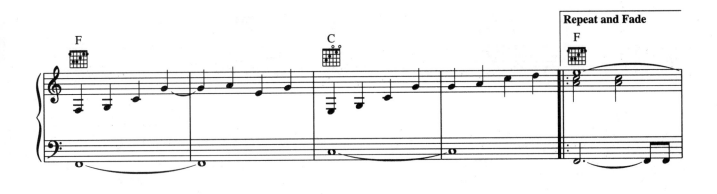

Repeat and Fade

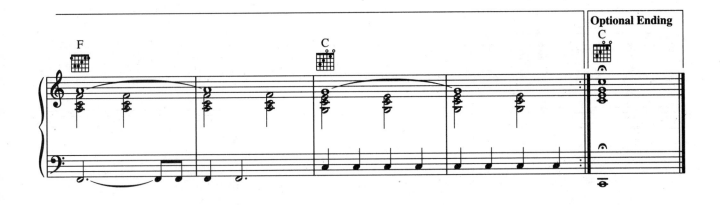

Optional Ending

RELEASE ME

Words and Music by ROBERT YOUNT,
EDDIE MILLER and DUB WILLIAMS

Please re- lease me, let me go, ___
I have found a new love, dear, ___
Please re- lease me, can't you see ___

___ for I don't love you an- y-
___ and I will al- ways want her
___ you'd be a fool to cling her

SAIL AWAY

Words and Music by
RAFE VAN HOY

rock - ing of the wa - ter, and dream of how our life___ will some - day

be, when she sails a - way___ with me.

As I
Then a

rit.

SINGING THE BLUES

Words and Music by
MELVIN ENDSLEY

SIXTEEN TONS

Words and Music by
MERLE TRAVIS

SLEEPING SINGLE IN A DOUBLE BED

Words and Music by DENNIS MORGAN
and KYE FLEMING

TALL, TALL TREES

Words and Music by GEORGE JONES
and ROGER MILLER

SWEET DREAMS

Words and Music by
DON GIBSON

TENNESSEE WALTZ

Words and Music by REDD STEWART
and PEE WEE KING

THREE CIGARETTES IN AN ASHTRAY

Words and Music by EDDIE MILLER
and W.S. STEVENSON

Two _____ cig - a - rettes in an ash - tray. _____

My __ love and I in a small _____ caf - é.

Then a strang - er _____ came a - long _____ and

TILL YOU LOVE ME

Words and Music by GARY BURR
and BOB DiPIERO

WALKING THE FLOOR OVER YOU

Words and Music by
ERNEST TUBB

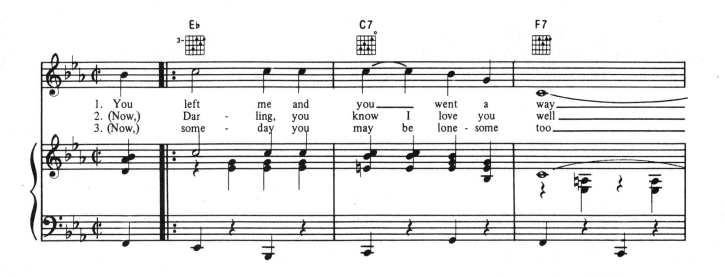

1. You left me and you____ went a way____
2. (Now,) Dar - ling, you know I love you well____
3. (Now,) some - day you may be lone - some too____

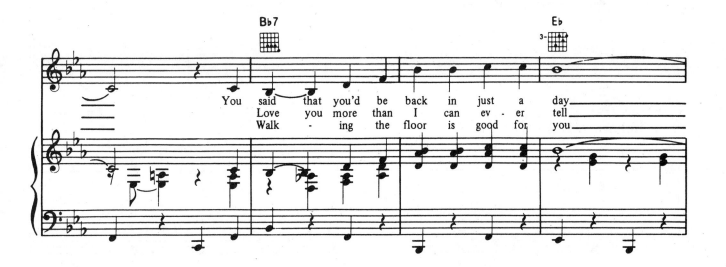

You said that you'd be back in just a day____
Love you more than I can ev - er tell____
Walk - ing the floor is good for you____

WALK A MILE IN MY SHOES

Words and Music by
JOE SOUTH

be sur-prised to see that you'd been blind.

Chorus

Walk A Mile In My Shoes, Walk A Mile In My Shoes,

And before you a-buse, crit-i-cize and ac-cuse,

Walk A Mile In My Shoes. Now your whole

ADDITIONAL LYRICS

2. Now your whole world you see around you is just a reflection
   And the law of karma says you reap just what you sow.
   So unless you've lived a life of total perfection
   You'd better be careful of every stone that you should throw.
   (Chorus)

3. And yet we spend the day throwing stones at one another
   'Cause I don't think or wear my hair the same way you do.
   Well I may be common people but I'm your brother
   And when you strike out and try to hurt me it's a-hurtin' you.
   (Chorus)

4. There are people on reservations and out in the ghettos
   And, brother, there but for the grace of God go you and I.
   If I only had the wings of a little angel
   Don't you know I'd fly to the top of the mountain and then I'd cry.
   (Chorus)

WALKIN' AFTER MIDNIGHT

Lyrics by DON HECHT
Music by ALAN W. BLOCK

WALKING IN THE SUNSHINE

Words and Music by
ROGER MILLER

WELCOME TO MY WORLD

Words and Music by RAY WINKLER
and JOHN HATHCOCK

WHO I AM

Words and Music by BRETT JAMES
and TROY VERGES

Moderately

If I live ____ to be ____ a hun-dred and nev-er
So when I make a big ____ mis-take, _____ when I

see the Sev-en Won-ders, that-'ll be ____ al-right. ____
fall flat on ____ my face, _____ I know I'll be ____ al-right.

WHAT MATTERED MOST

Words and Music by GARY BURR
and VINCE MELAMED

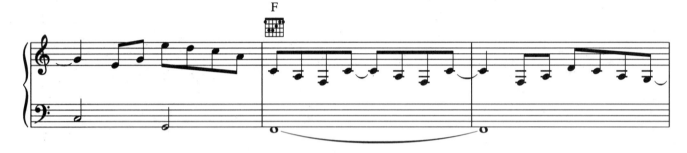

I thought __ I knew ___

the girl __ so _____ well.
she nev - er _____ said.

324

WHEN MY BLUE MOON TURNS TO GOLD AGAIN

Words and Music by WILEY WALKER
and GENE SULLIVAN

With movement

Mem-o-ries that lin-ger in my heart, _____ Mem-o-
lips that used to thrill me so, _____ Your
cas-tles we built of dreams to-geth-er _____ Were the

ries that make my heart grow cold; _____ But some day they'll
kiss-es were meant for on-ly me; _____ In my dreams they
sweet-est stor-ies ev-er told; _____ May-be we will

live a-gain, sweet-heart, _____ And my blue moon a-gain will turn to
live a-gain, sweet-heart, _____ But my gol-den moon is just a mem-o-
live them all a-gain, _____ And my blue moon a-gain will turn to

WRITE THIS DOWN

Words and Music by KENT ROBBINS
and DANA HUNT

YOU ARE MY SUNSHINE

Words and Music by JIMMIE DAVIS
and CHARLES MITCHELL

YOU HAD ME FROM HELLO

Words and

You Can't Make A Heart Love Somebody

Words and Music by STEVE CLARK
and JOHNNY MacRAE

Moderately slow

YOUR CHEATIN' HEART

Words and Music by
HANK WILLIAMS